Parts of Animals

1 Which body parts can you name?

Use this page to write or draw as many different body parts as you can think of.

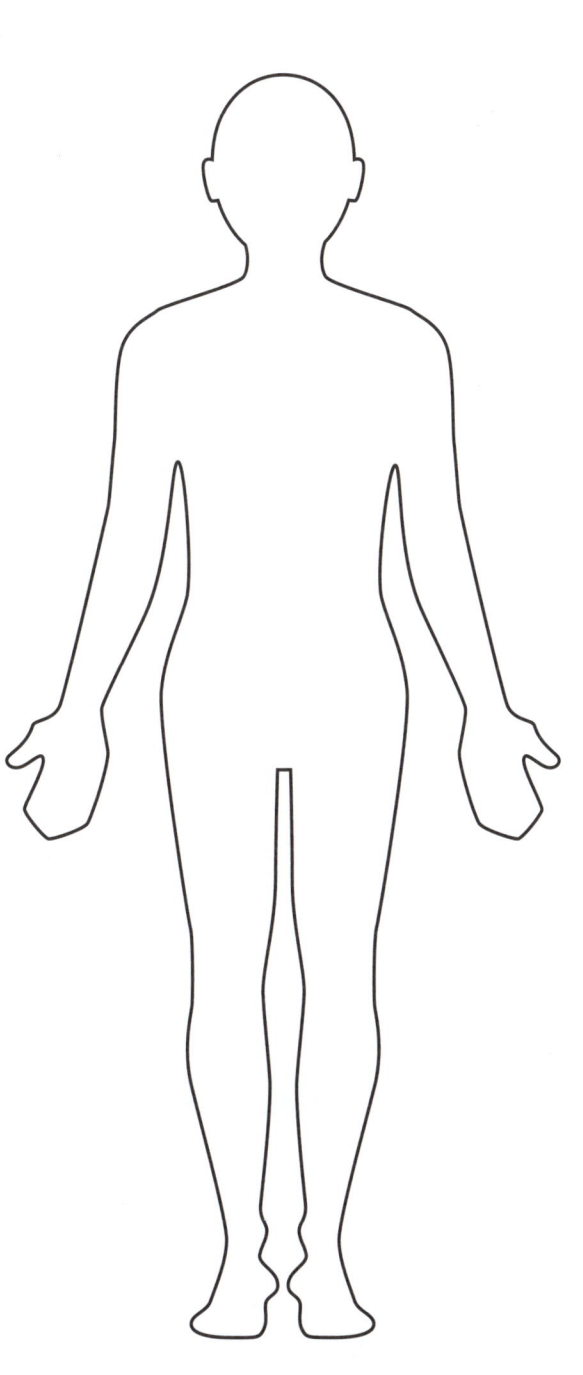

Brilliant Body Parts

Think of some activities you like to do, and which parts of your body you use.

1   Complete the sentences.

When I _____

I use my _____

to _____

When I _____

I use my _____

to _____

When I _____

I use my _____

to _____

Missing Body Parts

Try doing things using a different body part. Circle the faces below to describe how you found each activity.

1. Write your name holding a pencil between your toes.

2. Throw and catch a ball with your eyes closed.

3. Paint a picture holding the paint brush in your other hand.

Looking After Body Parts

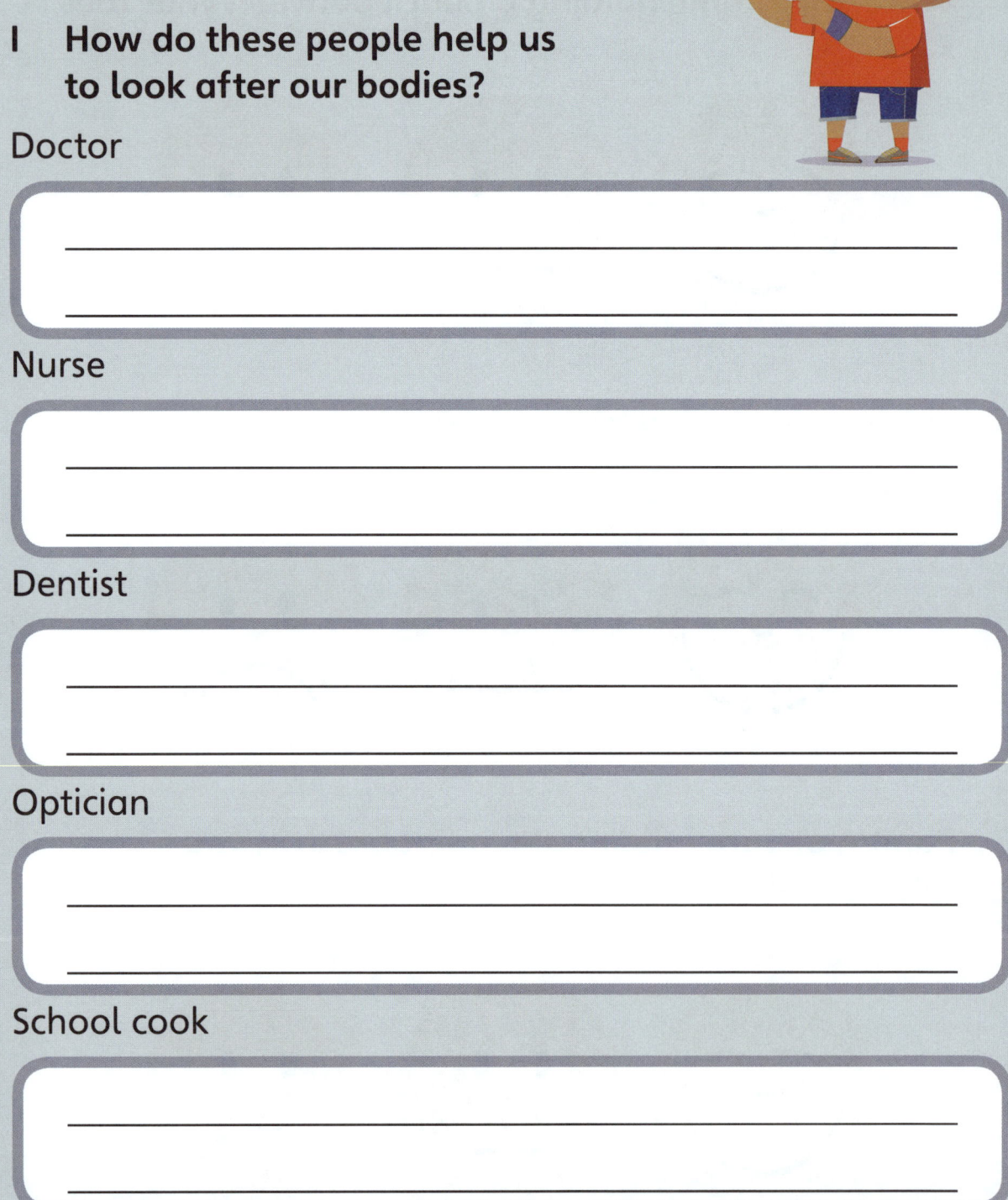

1. How do these people help us to look after our bodies?

Doctor

Nurse

Dentist

Optician

School cook

Ask a Vet

1 What does a vet do?

2 Plan two questions that you would like to ask a vet.

Our Senses

1. Use this page to plan what you would include in a poster to tell people about our five senses.

   Draw a diagram or write the name of the sense in the boxes below.

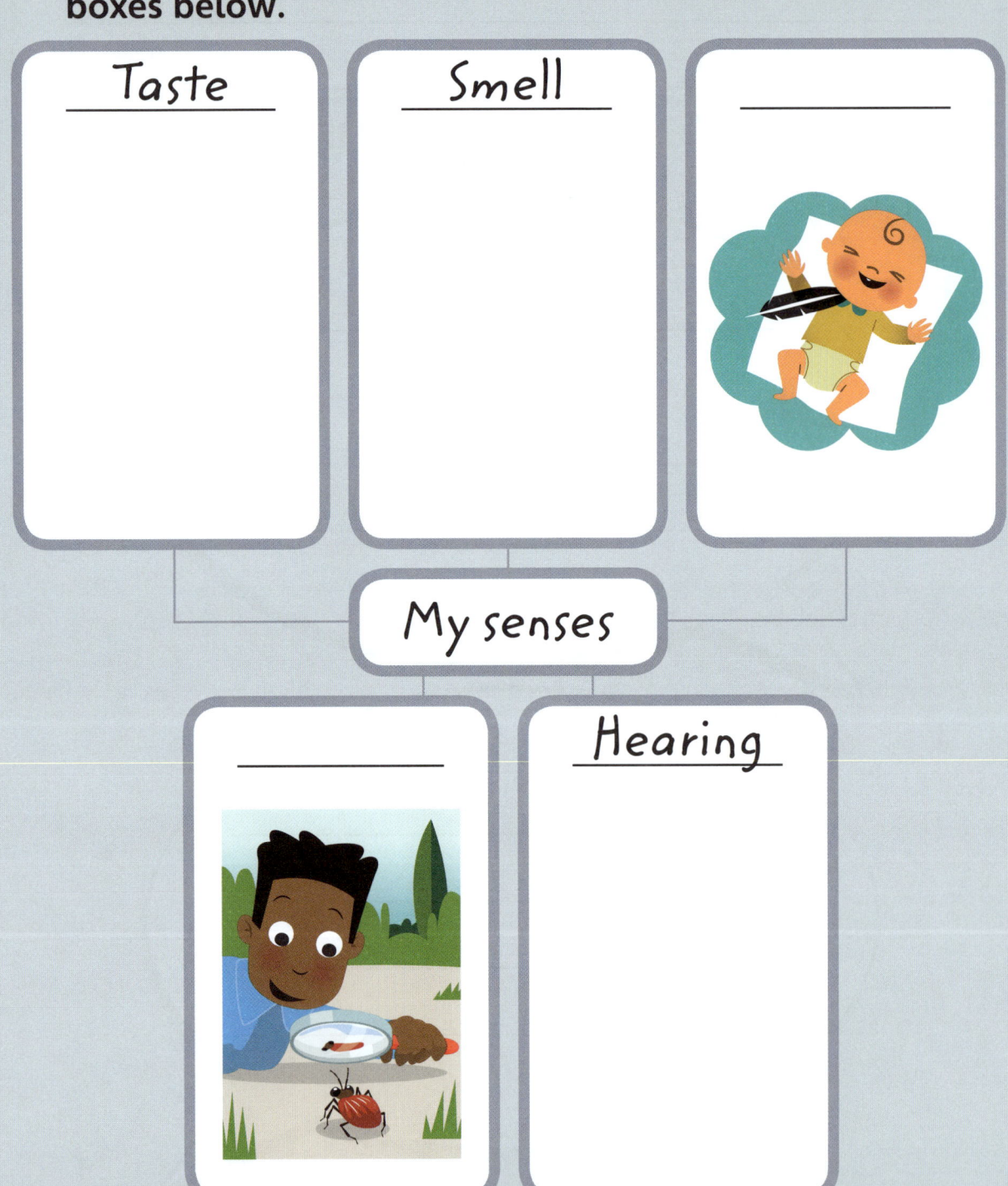

Parts of Animals

2   Draw lines to match the senses to the body parts.

eye

mouth

nose

skin

ear

3   Which is your favourite sense? Why?

Our Sense of Smell

1. Complete the table by adding ticks to show which smells you like and do not like.

	Nice smell	Nasty smell
honey		
hummus		
oranges		
coffee		

2. My favourite smell is

3. The smell I do not like is

4. Circle the smell that warns us of danger.

Our Sense of Taste

1. What is your favourite taste?

   My favourite taste is _____

2. What taste do you not like?

   The taste I do not like is _____

3. Circle the food below that tastes sweet.

Chocolate bar

Potato chips

Boiled egg

Jar of honey

Doughnut

Pita bread

Our Sense of Touch

1. Write some words to describe these objects.

A baby's blanket feels

☐

A rock feels

☐

A hair brush feels

☐

2. Do these objects feel rough or smooth?
   Put the words below into the correct column.
   The first one has been done for you.

   sand   cup   mirror   brick   sock

Rough	Smooth
Sand	

Parts of Animals

3 Use this page to plan how to make a barefoot walk with trays of different materials for your classmates to feel with their feet.
Draw and label your materials using the boxes below.

| Material 1 | will feel _____ |

| Material 2 | will feel _____ |

| Material 3 | will feel _____ |

| Material 4 | will feel _____ |

Our Sense of Sound

Go on a listening walk around your school.

1. List the sounds you can hear in different places around your school.

Place in school	Sound I can hear

2. Which was the loudest sound you heard?

3. Which was the quietest sound you heard?

Animal Parts

1. Which body parts do these animals have?
   Write each word in the correct box.

Goat

ears   horns   beard   hooves   tail   nose

Elephant

head   ears   tusks   feet   trunk   back

Diagrams – Record it!

1 When I label a picture or a diagram, I need to:

a _____

b _____

2a Draw a picture of your favourite animal.

2b Work like a scientist and label as many different body parts as you can.

Comparing Animal Parts

1 Which body parts do animals have that are:

a the same as humans?

b different from humans?

Put a ✓ in the tables below if the animal has that body part. Put a x if it does not.

The first one has been done for you.

Body part	Camel	Human
eyes	✓	✓
hump		
ears		
toes		

Body part	Fish	Human
fin	✓	x
mouth		
fingers		
feet		

What I Know About Parts of Animals

1. Draw a new animal made from lots of different animal body parts.

It could have the ears of an elephant, the wings of a bird and the claws of a tiger! You decide.

2. Label as many of the body parts as you can. Remember to include body parts used for its senses too!